Uzma's Photo Album

Ann Morris

Photographs by Heidi Larson

A&C Black · London

'That's my cousin, Basset, and Uncle Anwar in Pakistan – and here's where we stayed in Islamabad, the capital of Pakistan. We had such a good holiday.'

'Leave the pictures for now, Uzma,' says Ms Roosedale, her teacher. 'It's nearly time to go home. You can show them to the class another time.

'Do you think your mum would come in one day and help you tell everyone about your visit? You could show us all your photographs then.'

That night, Uzma tells her mum what Ms Roosedale has suggested.

'Will you come Mum? Could I show everyone the bangles we bought?' she asks. 'And the carving we bought for Aunty?'

'That's a good idea. I'd like to meet your class,' says Mum. 'We'll have to be careful with the carving. It's very special – a verse from the Koran. Let's wrap it up.'

4

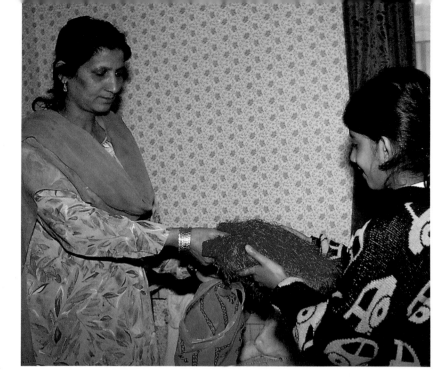

'Could we take the lovely pink cloth which you bought in the market? And I mustn't forget the pictures of Basset's birthday,' Uzma reminds herself.

A few days later, Uzma and her mum come to school together.

Mrs Rana, the children's Urdu teacher, also joins the class this morning. She wants to hear about Uzma's holiday.

Ms Roosedale
introduces Uzma's
mum, Mrs Aslam, to
the class.

Then she takes
the register.

'Now, let's see who's
here today.
Haroon?'
'Here.'
'Tara?'
'Here.'

After she has called
all the children's
names, she calls
Mrs Aslam's name.
'Here,' says Uzma's
mum, and the
children all laugh.

Ms Roosedale helps everyone find a place to sit where they can see. Mrs Aslam takes out the beautiful pink cloth which she bought in Pakistan.

'It feels so soft,' says Rupender.

Uzma is only half listening. She's thinking about the time when they bought the cloth. They went to a market in Murree, a village just outside Islamabad.

Mum spent a long time choosing, but the man at the stall didn't mind. He kept showing her the different rolls of cloth until she found just the one she wanted.

9

At the stall next door, Uzma noticed some beautiful bangles and Mum let her buy some to take back to England.

Then Uzma's sister, Afshan, and her cousin tried them on to see which they liked best.

Mrs Aslam has a whole boxful of bangles to show the children at school.

'Can I try some on?' asks Rekha. 'I have some like these at home. My dad brought them back from India.'

While the children are trying on the bangles, Sandeep asks, 'What's in that parcel wrapped in newspaper?'

Mrs Aslam explains that the writing on the carving is a verse from the Koran and that it is written in Arabic.

The letters look like the ones on the
newspaper. Mrs Rana explains that it's an
Urdu newspaper. She helps the children to
read a few of the Urdu words.

Then Uzma shows
the children some of
her photographs.
'This one is the
market at Murree,'
she says.

She remembers that
there were heaps of
spices, nuts and
different kinds of
fruit; pine nuts,
peanuts, pistachios,
apricots, pears and
oranges.

'We bought some peanuts,' she says. 'Dad told us not to eat too many or we would spoil our appetites. But he should have known that we were always hungry.'

Mum knew just the right place for lunch, right in the middle of the market.

Uncle Anwar said they could order anything they wanted.

Mum and Dad had chicken curry with nan and salad. Uzma ordered a hamburger with chips and, of course, everyone wanted some of her chips.

'But you still have lots more photographs. Can we see the rest?' asks Rupender.

'Well,' says Uzma. 'Here we are at the airport. That's my big brother, Imran, at the back. My two sisters, Afshan and Heena are next to Mum. We had to wait for ages at the airport because the 'plane was delayed.

'This is outside the house in Islamabad, with Uncle Anwar and Aunty Mumtaz. The girl next to Afshan is my cousin, Saima.

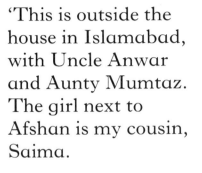

'And that's Imran again, outside the Faisal mosque. Isn't the mosque beautiful? It's the newest one in Islamabad.

'There's me and my sister, with some of my mum's family. They live in a village in the Punjab.

'We went to a wedding there. The groom in the wedding suit is my cousin Mohammed. He's wearing a garland made out of rupee notes! The little boy is Asan. He had to help Mohammed on the day.

'There were so many wedding presents. Here they are, laid out so that everyone can have a look.'

'Hey, look at that tractor!' says Raghbir.
'I wouldn't mind having a go on that.'

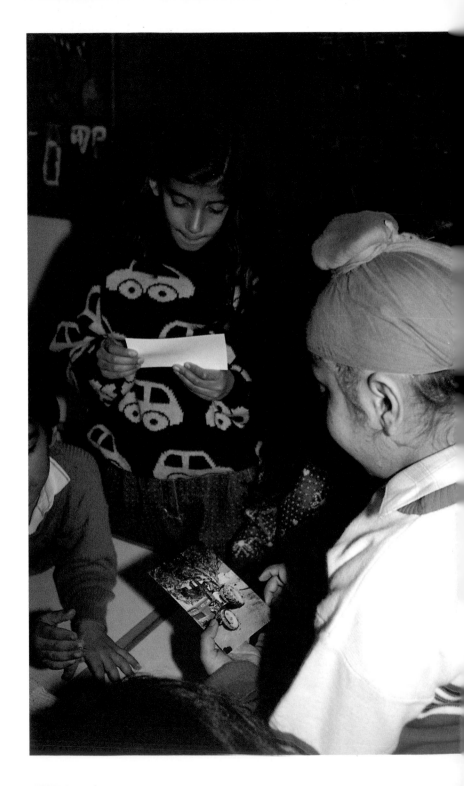

'Yes, Uncle Iqbal gave us a ride to his cotton fields, just outside the village,' says Uzma.

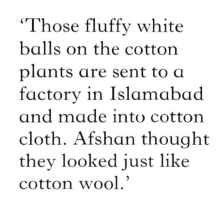

'Those fluffy white balls on the cotton plants are sent to a factory in Islamabad and made into cotton cloth. Afshan thought they looked just like cotton wool.'

23

The last picture is of Basset's birthday party, back in Islamabad. Uzma explains how he cut his own cake even though he was only four years old. 'And we sang happy birthday to you!' she says.

It's time for Mrs Aslam to go home, so Ms Roosedale thanks her and Uzma for a lovely time.

Uzma feels very pleased, and also proud of her mum.

'Do you think Uncle and Aunty will invite me back to Pakistan next year?' she asks on the way home. 'Then I could take some more pictures for my photo album.'